To Jill
—G.M.

For Paul, a good money manager
—M.H.

Copyright © 1998 by Scholastic Inc.
The activities on pages 27–32 copyright © 1998 by Marilyn Burns.
All rights reserved. Published by Scholastic Inc.
Printed in the U.S.A.

ISBN 0-439-70142-2

1 2 3 4 5 6 7 8 9 10   23   12 11 10 09 08 07 06 05 04

Monster Money

by Grace Maccarone
Illustrated by Marge Hartelius
Math Activities by Marilyn Burns

SCHOLASTIC INC.
New York Toronto London Auckland Sydney
Mexico City New Delhi Hong Kong Buenos Aires

Good morning! Good morning!
Ten cents for a pet,
a monster's best friend.
Which one will you get?

Ten pennies buy a frog.

Ten pennies buy a slug.

Five pennies and one nickel
buy a bug.

Two nickels buy a fly.

Two nickels buy a flea.

One nickel and five pennies
buy a bee.

One dime buys a beetle.

One dime buys a bat.

Five pennies and one nickel
buy a rat.

Ten pennies buy a crab.

Two nickels buy a jellyfish.

One nickel and five pennies
buy a smelly fish.

One dime buys a jiggly thing.

Ten pennies buy a wiggly thing.

Five pennies and one nickel
buy a giggly thing.

Ten cents buy a pet,
a monster's best friend.
Take your pet home
because this is the end!

• ABOUT THE ACTIVITIES •

Children need many experiences in order to learn about our money system. They need to become familiar with our different coins, understand how much each is worth, and learn about the purchasing power of money. Understanding money is complicated for young children for several reasons. The names of the coins — *penny, nickel,* and *dime* — do not provide children with helpful clues about how much each coin is worth. Also, the smallest coin, the dime, is worth more than the others. And having more coins doesn't necessarily mean having more money—an especially difficult concept for young children who have recently learned about the power of counting.

Monster Math provides one of the many experiences children need to build their understanding of pennies, nickels, and dimes. The activities in this section offer additional support for learning. To do the activities and games, you'll need a small paper lunch bag, a small paper cup, and a collection of coins — about 3 dimes, 6 nickels, and 25 pennies.

Children enjoy doing their favorite activities over and over, and the repeat experiences provide them with useful practice. Also, the **Hello Reader! Math** book *A Quarter from the Tooth Fairy* is another enjoyable way to extend your child's learning about money. Be open to your child's interests, and have fun with math!

—Marilyn Burns

You'll find tips and suggestions
for guiding the activities whenever
you see a box like this!

Retelling the Story

There are lots of pets to buy in the Monster Pet Store. Read through the story again. Put the coins you need to buy each pet on the pictures below. Each time, count up the money the pet costs.

a smelly fish	a frog
one nickel and five pennies	ten pennies
a flea	a bat
two nickels	one dime
a jiggly thing	a giggly thing
one dime	five pennies and one nickel

No Peeking!

This is a game for two people. You need a small paper lunch bag with three pennies, three nickels, and three dimes in it. One person names a coin — penny, nickel, or dime. The other reaches into the lunch bag and, without peeking, tries to remove one of those coins. Take turns.

How Many? How Much?

Ask a grown-up to give you all of the pennies, nickels, and dimes in his or her pocket or purse. (Don't forget to say that you will give back the coins when you're done.)

Sort the coins so that the pennies are in one pile, the nickels are in another, and the dimes are in yet another. Then try answering these questions:

How many pennies do you have?
How much money are the pennies worth?

How many nickels do you have?
How much money are the nickels worth?

How many dimes are there?
How much money are the dimes worth?

Playing this game regularly with your child will give him or her much needed practice identifying coins and counting money. To extend the activity, have your child figure along with you to see how much money the coins are worth all together.

Ten Penny Riddles

In the story, with ten pennies you can buy a frog, a slug, a crab, or a wiggly thing. But the monsters below don't have enough pennies. Guess how many more pennies they need for each pet. Then put down the extra pennies and count up to make sure you have ten all together.

a frog

a slug

a wiggly thing

What's Under the Cup?

This is a game for two people. You need one small paper cup upside down in between you. Also, each of you should put ten pennies in a row in front of you.

One of you hides some of your ten pennies under the cup. Leave the other pennies out so the other person can count them. The other person guesses how many pennies are hidden under the cup. Then pick up the cup and count to check.

Takes turns hiding and guessing.

A hint: You can use your own pennies to help you guess.

Coin Rubbing

You can use a crayon to make good rubbings of coins. Try it! Place a sheet of paper on top of a coin. Ask a grown-up to hold the paper and coin in place. Then use a crayon to rub on the part of the paper that is covering the coin. Do this for the front and back of a penny, nickel, and dime. Then use your coins or rubbings to answer these riddles.

Coin Riddles

Which coin is worth ONE CENT? (See if you can find where it says ONE CENT on the back.)

Which coin is a dime?

Find the coins that have a building on the back.

Which coin is a penny?

Which coin is worth FIVE CENTS? (See if you can find where it says FIVE CENTS on the back.)

There is a picture of a United States president on the front of each coin. Which two coins have the presidents facing the same way?

Find the coin that is worth TEN CENTS.

Which coin is a nickel?